The Power of Gratitude

Unlocking Hidden Treasures

A Grateful
Heart is
A Happy
Heart
♡ Ruth
Maille

By **Ruth Maille**
Art by **Pencil Master Studio**

Illustrations by Pardeep Mehra
Designed by Priyam Mehra

Publisher's Cataloging-in-Publication data

Names: Maille, Ruth, author. | Mehra, Pardeep, illustrator.
Title: The power of gratitude : unlocking hidden treasures / written by Ruth Maille; illustrated by Pardeep Mehra.
Series: The Power Of
Description: Bristol, RI: Orbit Publishing, 2021. | Summary: An ABC book centered around children's understanding of the concept of gratitude and discovering the things for which they feel most grateful.
Identifiers: LCCN: 2021920961 | ISBN: 978-1-955299-07-7 (hardcover) | 978-1-955299-06-0 (paperback) | 978-1-955299-05-3 (ebook)
Subjects: LCSH Gratitude--Juvenile literature. | Kindness--Juvenile literature. | Emotions--Juvenile literature. | Alphabet. | BISAC JUVENILE FICTION / Concepts / Alphabet | JUVENILE FICTION / Social Themes / Values & Virtues | JUVENILE FICTION / Social Themes / Emotions & Feelings
Classification: LCC BF575.G68 M35 2021 | DDC 179/.9--dc23

Dedication

To the children of our world, you have amazing superpowers. Keep sharing them with others.

Other Books by **Ruth Maille**

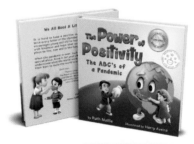

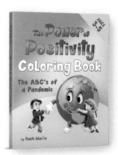
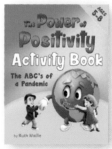

Sign up to be notified about future books released at

www.ruthmaille-author.com

✉ **ruthmaille@gmail.com**

f **@RuthAnnSimonelliMailleauthor**

@ruth.maille

Bristol Rhode Island USA +1-401-556-0084

Orbit is excited about his new adventure. He is visiting a sleepover camp and everyone is excited to see him.

Orbit gathers the children under a beautiful oak tree. "Today I would like to talk to you about gratitude," says Orbit. "What do YOU think gratitude means?"

Matilda jumps up and shouts, "I know that word. Gratitude means being thankful for the people and things in our lives!"

"Yes Matilda, that is exactly what gratitude means. But there is even more," says Orbit.

"Gratitude is also a FEELING. When we are grateful, we feel warm and snuggly inside."

"Should we still feel grateful when sad things happen?" asks Trent.

"Yes, we can still feel grateful, even when things don't go as we planned.

What if you are excited about your soccer game, but then it rains and you can't play?

As disappointing as that might be, you can choose to look at the positive side;
you can feel grateful that you don't have to be outside in the cold, wet air, and happy that you now have time to go to a movie."

"Practicing gratitude is like exercising your muscles. The more you practice, the better you become. Once you start looking, you will find things to be grateful for EVERYWHERE!

It is like going on a treasure hunt. The more you look the better you get at finding gratitude in your life."

"Who would like to go on a gratitude hunt with me?" asks Orbit. Everyone raises their hand.
"Here is how we play. I'll tell you a letter, along with a word that begins with that letter, and YOU use that word to tell me why you are grateful."
Everyone listens carefully as Orbit begins:

Dominic raises his hand. "Acorns grow into giant oak trees. We are grateful to have picnics under an oak tree because the big leaves give us shade and keep us cool."

"Very nice," says Orbit, "and I'm sure the squirrels are grateful for the acorns that fall from oak trees."

B is for Brain

Matilda says, "I am grateful for my brain because it makes me curious and helps me think and learn."

"Yes," says Orbit, "and I'm sure you are all grateful for the nourishing food that your mom gives you to keep your brain healthy."

C is for Cloud

"I am grateful for clouds," says Colin. "They make me happy because they look so soft and fluffy. Sometimes they even look like animals."

Orbit smiles. "If you watch clouds carefully," he says, "you often see them change into all kinds of shapes and forms. I'll bet you are grateful that you can spend time outdoors with your family."

D is for Darkness

"I am grateful for darkness because I like to go outside at night and count the stars with my dad," says David.

"If you ever feel sad," says Orbit, "the brightness of those stars might be just the thing to make you feel grateful for the happy times in your life."

E is for Earth Day

Mac waves his hand in the air. "If Earth Day is about the Earth, we should all feel grateful to live on this beautiful planet," he says. "We should do our part by picking up litter and planting more trees."

Orbit nods his head and says, "Every year on April 22nd, we celebrate Earth Day. It's a special day that reminds us that our planet needs special care. We should be grateful for our planet and do what we can to protect it."

F is for Finger

Matilda says, "I'm grateful for my fingers—all 10 of them! They help me count."

"I use my fingers to point, and pick things up and I can even wiggle them," says Kim.

"I use my fingers to help me to talk to my friend in sign language," shouts Sawyer.

Orbit looks pleased. He says, "I'm sure your friend is grateful that you care enough to learn his language."

G is for Garden

Trent says, "I help my Mom in our garden. Everyone in my family is grateful to have enough food to eat. We always share our fruits and vegetables with our neighbors and other people who don't have as much as we have."

"That's very nice. I am sure they are very grateful for the food you share with them from your garden," says Orbit.

H is for Honeybee

"Honeybees pollinate our flowers, fruits, and vegetables," says Dominic, "and I am very grateful for that."

"Exactly," says Orbit. "As honeybees move from plant to plant in search of nectar, they leave behind grains of pollen. Then the plants grow and produce flowers and food. I know we are grateful for all the wonderful plants—and the delicious honey."

I is for Imagination

Sawyer is excited. "I am grateful for my imagination because I can pretend I just won a medal in the Winter Olympics for ice skating."

"Yes, anything is possible when you use your imagination," says Orbit.

J is for Jack-o-lantern

"I am grateful for jack-o-lanterns," says Rosie. "After Halloween, I plant the pumpkin seeds in the ground instead of throwing them in the garbage. Tiny sprouts come up in the spring and by fall we have our own pumpkins to share with friends."

"And I am grateful to be one of those friends because I love pumpkin pie," says Orbit.

19

K is for Kindness

Amelia raises her hand. "I am grateful for the kindness of all my friends," she says. "They share their time, and play with me—especially when I feel sad."

"Kindness is important to friendship," says Orbit. "You are lucky to have kind friends."

L is for Ladybug

Rosie smiles and says, "I am grateful for ladybugs because they help gardeners like my Grandma. Ladybugs eat the insects that like to eat our plants."

"I'll bet you didn't know that ladybugs aren't always red," says Orbit. "They can also be orange or black, and they don't always have spots."

M is for Music

"Don't you just love music?" shouts Dominic. "When I was a baby, I liked lullabies and nursery rhymes. Now that I am a big kid, I am grateful for songs that make me want to jump and dance, like the Hokey Pokey!"

Orbit begins to dance around. "I am grateful for music too," he says laughing.

N is for Number

"I am grateful for numbers because they help me count. I need numbers when I count the days until grandma and grandpa visit," laughs Mac.

"That's a great example," says Orbit. "I am also grateful for the numbers on my clock that show me what time it is."

O is for Oval

"I know!" says Kim, waving her hand in the air. "I saw a momma bird with an egg that had fallen out of her nest. The oval shape of the egg kept it from rolling away in the grass. I am grateful that the egg was safe."

"I'm sure the momma bird was grateful too," says Orbit.

P is for Puddle

Dominic says, "I am grateful for puddles when it rains. I like to jump and make huge splashes!" "Me too," giggled Rosie.

Orbit smiles as he says, "I'm sure you are all grateful for BIG puddles which make the biggest splashes."

Q is for Question

"My mom says it's good to ask questions because it means I am curious. She says being curious is a good thing," says Matilda, "so I am grateful for being able to ask questions."

"Great answer," says Orbit. "I'm grateful that all of you like to answer questions."

R is for Rainforest

"I am grateful for the rainforest," says Mac. "It's the home of a lot of unique trees, plants, and animals. My favorite animal is the red-eyed tree frog."

"I know what you mean," says Orbit. "We are all grateful that the animals have a safe home in the rainforest. Did you know that the red-eyed tree frog is sometimes called a monkey frog because it can jump so far?"

S is for Snowflake

Rosie says, "My aunt told me that no two snowflakes are alike. I think that's pretty cool. I am grateful that snowflakes are different and unique."

"Just like us!" says Orbit. "We are all grateful to be our own individual selves."

T is for Train

"I am grateful for trains," says Trent. "My favorite toy is my train set. I sometimes pretend my trains are traveling through cities, farms, and parks."

"One day, perhaps you will all travel on a big train," says Orbit.

U is for Utensil

"I know what that means!" says Amelia. "That's something we eat with. My favorite utensil is a spoon. I am grateful for a spoon every time I get to eat ice cream out of a bowl!"

"I am grateful for spoons too," says Orbit, with a wink and a smile. "I think spoons are friendlier utensils than forks or knives."

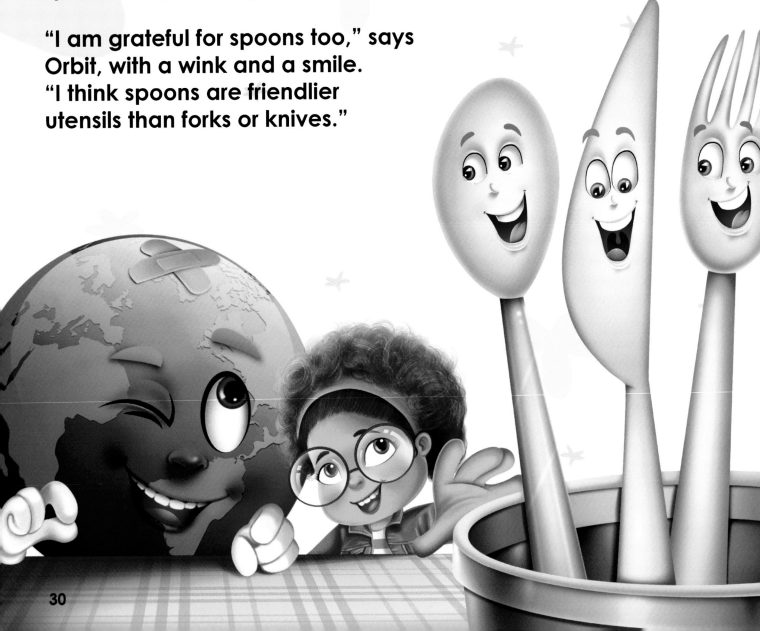

V is for Vacation

Colin is anxious to share. "My family just had a vacation in a cabin in the woods. I am grateful that we toasted marshmallows around the campfire and went on hikes."

"Vacations are so much fun," adds Orbit. "We are all grateful that we are having a little vacation right here at camp."

W is for Wind

"I am grateful for the wind because my friend Kim and I can fly our kites when the wind blows," says Trent."

"We might not be able to see the wind, but we know it's there," says Orbit. "We are all grateful for the wind when it blows on hot summer days."

X is for Kiss

"What?" shouts Matilda. "How can X be for kiss?"
"Kiss begins with the letter K!" shouts Trent.
Orbit has a big grin on his face. "Well, you're right," he says, "but we also use the letter X to mean kiss. And here's another secret—we can also use the letter O to mean hug. When we write the letters XOXO, it means KISSES and HUGS."

"Wow, I am grateful that my Mommy and Daddy write XOXO on my birthday cards and for their kisses and hugs," says Matilda.

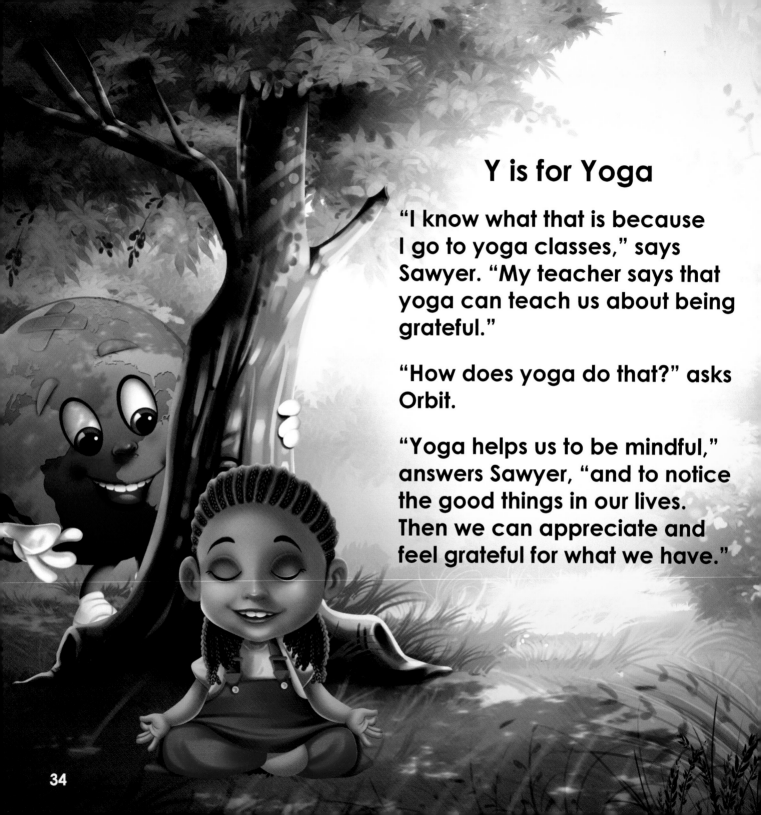

Y is for Yoga

"I know what that is because I go to yoga classes," says Sawyer. "My teacher says that yoga can teach us about being grateful."

"How does yoga do that?" asks Orbit.

"Yoga helps us to be mindful," answers Sawyer, "and to notice the good things in our lives. Then we can appreciate and feel grateful for what we have."

Z is for Zipper

"Oh, I am grateful for zippers—especially in the winter!" says Dominic excitedly. "I zip up my jacket and I stay nice and warm."

"You're right, Dominic. Zippers can be found on all kinds of things besides clothes—like backpacks, luggage, pillows, and so much more," says Orbit.

"Wow, boys and girls, great job!" says Orbit. "We have come to the end of the alphabet. It is time for me to head for home. You have shared some wonderful examples of gratitude. When you go home, you can share these ideas with your family and friends. Then they can become gratitude treasure hunters too."

As Orbit waves goodbye to the children, he shouts, "See you on our next adventure!"

About the author

As a pre-school teacher, Ruth Maille understands the importance of teaching young children about gratitude. Her previous award winning books The Power Of Positivity and The Power of Kindness have been featured in numerous blogs and online news articles about character traits that are important to learn as children.

Her goal is to share the knowledge she has gained from her experiences with children and parents, and to enable children to better understand and control their feelings.

Ruth enjoys spending time with her 2 sons and daughter, traveling, and exploring new places.

About the illustrator

Pardeep Mehra is the founder of **Pencil Master Digital Studio**, a family-owned business employing a large group of talented artists providing end-to-end illustration and publishing services.
For more than 15 years, Pardeep has been providing his keen eye, visualization and digital art skills to create hundreds of beautifully illustrated books that delight children all over the world. Pardeep lives in India with his wife Priyam and daughter Mehar.

For more info and portfolio review, visit
www.pencilmasterdigi.com